NURSERY SONGS

Arranged by Leah Gale
Illustrated by Corinne Malvern

A GOLDEN BOOK · NEW YORK

Western Publishing Company, Inc.
Racine, Wisconsin 53404

THE LITTLE GOLDEN BOOKS
ARE PREPARED UNDER THE SUPERVISION OF
MARY REED, Ph.D.
ASSISTANT PROFESSOR OF EDUCATION
TEACHERS COLLEGE, COLUMBIA UNIVERSITY

A COMMEMORATIVE FACSIMILE EDITION PUBLISHED ON THE OCCASION OF
THE 50TH ANNIVERSARY OF LITTLE GOLDEN BOOKS

LONDON BRIDGE

Singing Game

Lon-don Bridge is fall-ing down, Fall-ing down, fall-ing down,

Lon - don Bridge is fall - ing down, My fair la - dy.

London Bridge is half built up, etc.

London Bridge is all built up, etc.

Here's a prisoner I have got, etc.

Take the keys and lock her up, etc.

BILLY BOY

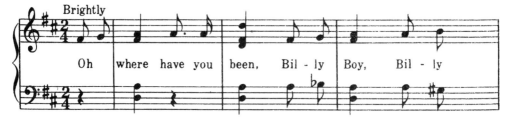

Brightly

Oh where have you been, Bil - ly Boy, Bil - ly

Boy? Oh where have you been, charm - ing Bil - ly? I have

been to seek a wife, She's the dar - ling of my life, She's a

young thing And can-not leave her moth-er.

Can she bake a cherry pie,
Billy Boy, Billy Boy?
Can she bake a cherry pie,
Charming Billy?

She can bake a cherry pie
In the twinkling of an eye,
But she's a young thing
And cannot leave her mother

MARY HAD A LITTLE

Rather fast

Ma-ry had a lit-tle lamb, lit-tle lamb, lit-tle lamb,

Everywhere that Mary went,
Mary went, Mary went,

Everywhere that Mary went
The lamb was sure to go.

LAMB

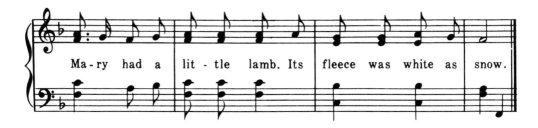

Ma-ry had a lit-tle lamb. Its fleece was white as snow.

He followed her to school one day;   It made the children laugh and play
That was against the rule;   To see a lamb at school.

7

OLD KING COLE

Old King Cole was a mer-ry old soul, And a

mer-ry old soul was he. He called for his pipe, and he

called for his bowl, And he called for his fid - dlers

three. Ev' - ry fid - dler had a fid-dle fine, And a

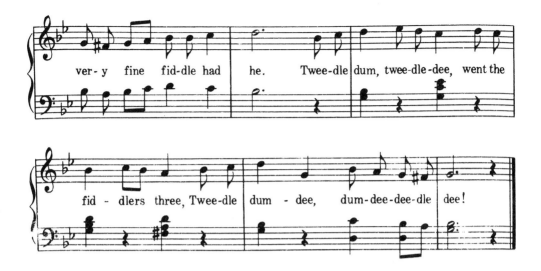

ver-y fine fid-dle had he. Twee-dle dum, twee-dle-dee, went the fid-dlers three, Twee-dle dum - dee, dum-dee-dee-dle dee!

Old King Cole was a merry old soul,
    And a merry old soul was he.
He called for his pipe, and he called for his bowl,
    And he called for his harpers three.
Ev'ry harper had a fine harp.
    And a very fine harp had he,
Twang-a-twang, twang-a-twang, went the harpers three,
    Twang-a-twang, twang, twang-a-twang-a twee.

Old King Cole was a merry old soul,
    And a merry old soul was he.
He called for his pipe, and he called for his bowl,
    And he called for his drummers three.
Ev'ry drummer had a fine drum,
    And a very fine drum had he,
Rub-a-dub, rub-a-dub went the drummers three,
    Rub-a-dub, dub, rub-a-dub-a dee.

A-HUNTING WE WILL GO

Briskly

Oh! a -hunt - ing we will go, A-

hunt-ing we will go. We'll catch a lit - tle fox, And

put him in a box, And then we'll let him go.

WHERE, O WHERE
HAS MY LITTLE DOG GONE?

O where, O where has my lit - tle dog gone? O

where, O where can he be?____ With his ears cut short and his

tail cut long, O where, O where can he be?____

JINGLE BELLS! JINGLE BELLS!

Brightly

Dash - ing thro' the snow, In a one - horse o - pen sleigh,

O'er the fields we go, Laugh - ing all the way;

Bells on bob - tail ring, Mak - ing spir - its bright; What

fun it is to ride and sing A sleigh - ing song to - night!

Jin-gle bells! Jin-gle bells! Jin-gle all the way!

O what fun it is to ride In a one-horse o-pen sleigh, O!

Jin-gle bells! Jin-gle bells! Jin-gle all the way!

O! what fun it is to ride In a one-horse o-pen sleigh! Hey!

O SUSANNA

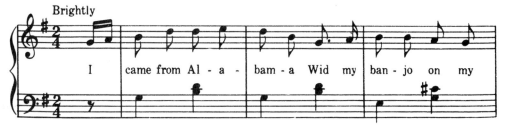

Brightly

I came from Al - a - bam - a Wid my ban - jo on my

knee, I'm g'wan to Lou - si - an - a My true love for to

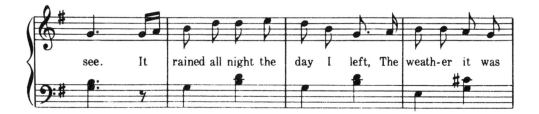

see. It rained all night the day I left, The weath-er it was

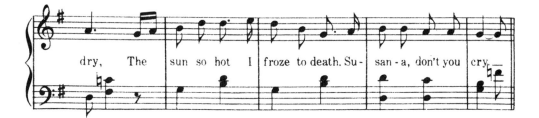

dry, The sun so hot I froze to death. Su - san-a, don't you cry

Chorus

Oh! Su - san - a, Oh! don't you cry for me. I've

come from Al - a - bam - a Wid my ban-jo on my knee.

CRADLE SONG

Slowly

Sleep, ba - by sleep, Thy fa - ther tends the

sheep, Thy moth - er shakes the dream - land tree, And

down come love - ly dreams for thee. Sleep, ba - by,

sleep.

Sleep, baby, sleep,
    And you shall have a sheep,
And he shall have a golden bell,
    And play with baby in the dell;
Sleep, baby, sleep.

I HAD
A LITTLE
NUT TREE

In moderate time

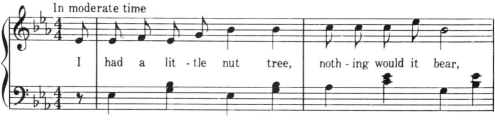

I had a lit - tle nut tree, noth - ing would it bear,

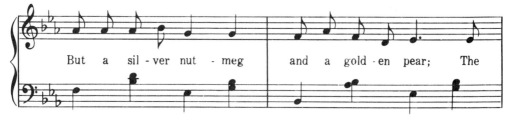

But a sil - ver nut - meg and a gold - en pear; The

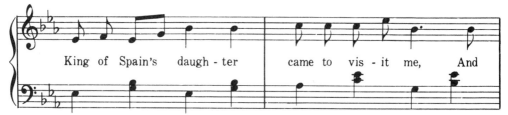

King of Spain's daugh - ter came to vis - it me, And

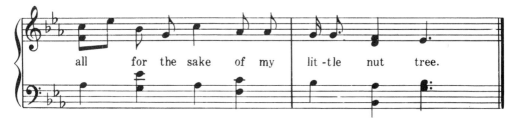

all for the sake of my lit - tle nut tree.

THE MULBERRY BUSH

Brightly

Here we go round the mul-ber-ry bush, The mul-ber-ry bush, the mul-ber-ry bush, Here we go round the mul-ber-ry bush, So ear-ly in ___ the morn-ing.

This is the way we scrub our clothes, etc.

This is the way we hang our clothes, etc.

This is the way we iron our clothes, etc.

ROW, ROW, ROW YOUR BOAT

Row, row, row your boat, Gen - tly down the stream,

Mer - ri - ly, mer - ri - ly, mer - ri - ly, mer - ri - ly —

Life is but a dream.

BROTHER JOHN
(Frère Jacques)

Are you sleep - ing, are you sleep - ing, Broth - er

John? Broth - er John? Morn - ing bells are ring - ing, morning bells are

ring - ing, Ding, ding, dong, Ding, ding, dong.

Frère Jacques, frère Jacques,
Dormez-vous? dormez-vous?
Sonnez les matines, sonnez les matines,
Din, din, don, Din, din don.

22

HERE WE GO LOOBY-LOO

Rather fast

Here we go Loo - by Loo ___ Here we go Loo - by Light ___

1.   FINE for last verse only

Here we go Loo - by Loo, ___ All on a Sat - ur - day night. ___ night.

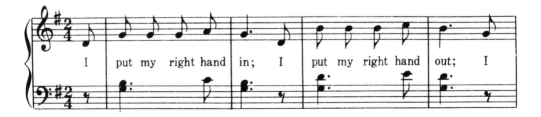

I put my right hand in; I put my right hand out; I

give my hand a | shake, shake, shake, And | turn my - self a - | bout. Oh,

D.C. al Fine

I put my left hand in, etc.

I put my right foot in, etc.

I put my left foot in, etc.

I put my whole self in, etc.

I put my whole self out, etc.

I give myself a shake, shake, shake,

And turn myself about, etc.

 ## LAVENDER'S BLUE

Quickly

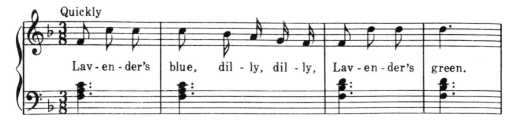

Lav - en - der's | blue, dil - ly, dil - ly, | Lav - en - der's | green.

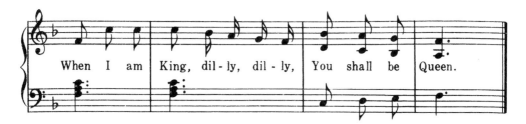

When I am | King, dil - ly, dil - ly, | You shall be | Queen.

Call up your men, dilly, dilly,
   Set them to work—
Some to the plow, dilly, dilly,
   Some to the cart,

Some to make hay, dilly, dilly,
   Some to cut corn,
While you and I, dilly, dilly,
   Keep ourselves warm.

TEN LITTLE INDIANS

Rather fast

One lit-tle, two lit-tle, three lit-tle In - dians;

Four lit - tle, five lit - tle, six lit - tle In - dians;

Seven lit - tle, eight lit - tle, nine lit - tle In - dians,

Ten lit - tle In - dian boys.

Ten little, nine little, eight little Indians,
Seven little, six little, five little Indians,
Four little, three little, two little Indians,
One little Indian boy.

O HOW LOVELY IS THE EVENING

O how love - ly is the eve - ning, is the

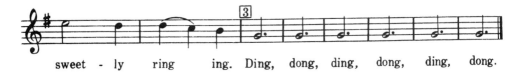

POP! GOES THE WEASEL

nee - dle, That's the way the mon - ey goes. Pop! goes the wea - sel.

THE FARMER IN THE DELL

The farm-er in the dell,___ The farm-er in the

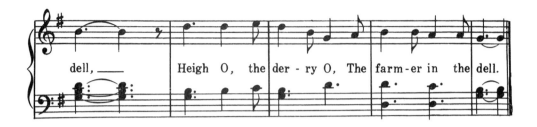

dell, _____ Heigh O, the der - ry O, The farm-er in the dell.

The farmer takes a wife, etc.

The wife takes a child, etc.

The child takes a nurse, etc.

The nurse takes a dog, etc.

The dog takes a cat, etc.

The cat takes a rat, etc.

The rat takes the cheese, etc.

The farmer runs away, etc.

The wife runs away, etc.

The cheese stands alone, etc.

SING A SONG OF SIXPENCE

The King was in his parlor
  Counting out his money;
The Queen was in the kitchen
  Eating bread and honey;

The maid was in the garden
  Hanging out the clothes;
Along came a blackbird
  And pecked off her nose.

OH DEAR WHAT CAN THE MATTER BE?

Oh! dear, what can the mat-ter be? Oh! dear, what can the mat-ter be? Oh! dear, what can the mat-ter be? John-ny's so long at the fair.___ He prom-ised to bring me a bas-ket of po-sies, A gar-land of li-lies, a gar-land of ro-ses, He prom-ised to bring me a

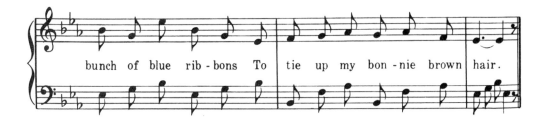

bunch of blue rib-bons To tie up my bon-nie brown hair.

A FROG WENT WALKING ON A SUMMER'S DAY

Brightly

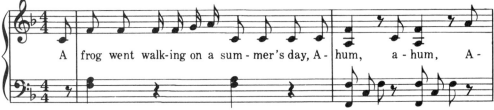

A frog went walk-ing on a sum-mer's day, A - hum, a - hum, A -

frog went walk-ing on a sum-mer's day, He met Miss Mous-ie on the way, A -

hum, a - hum, a - hum, a - hum, a - hum.

36

He said, "Miss Mousie, will you marry me?'
    A-hum, a-hum.
He said, "Miss Mousie, will you marry me?
We'll live together in an apple tree."
    A-hum, a-hum, a-hum, a-hum, a-hum.

The first to the wedding was Mr. Dick.
    A-hum, a-hum.
The first to the wedding was Mr. Dick;
He ate so much he nearly got sick.
    A-hum, a-hum, a-hum, a-hum, a-hum.

And what do you think they had for supper?
    A-hum, a-hum.
And what do you think they had for supper?
A fried mosquito and bread and butter.
    A-hum, a-hum, a-hum, a-hum, a-hum.

And what do you think they had on the shelf?
    A-hum, a-hum.
And what do you think they had on the shelf?
If you want to know, go look for yourself.
    A-hum, a-hum, a-hum, a-hum, a-hum.

DID YOU EVER SEE A LASSIE?

Did you ev - er see a las - sie, a las - sie, a

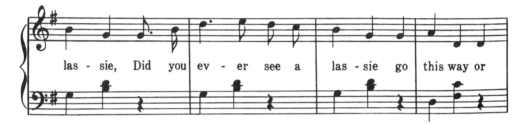

las - sie, Did you ev - er see a las - sie go this way or

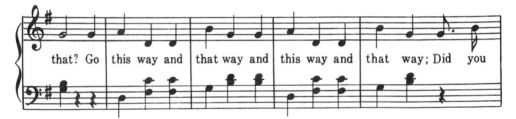

that? Go this way and that way and this way and that way; Did you

ev - er see a las - sie go this way and that?

Did you ever see a laddie, a laddie, a laddie,
Did you ever see a laddie go this way or that?
Go this way and that way and this way and that way;
Did you ever see a laddie go this way and that?

I LOVE LITTLE PUSSY

Brightly

I love lit - tle pus - sy, Her coat is so warm, And

if I don't hurt her, She'll do me no harm. I'll sit by the fire And

give her some food, And pus - sy will love me, Be- cause I am good.

DINGA-DINGA-DOODLE

Brightly

Did you ev - er see a cow in the sky?

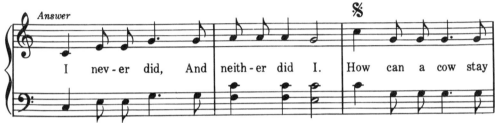

I nev - er did, And neith - er did I. How can a cow stay

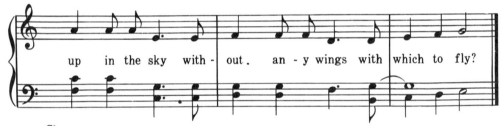

up in the sky with - out. an - y wings with which to fly?

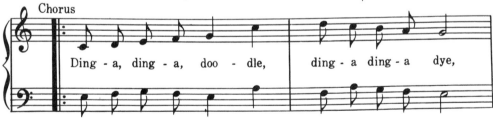

Ding - a, ding - a, doo - dle, ding - a ding - a dye,

She would fall if she did try.

Did you ever see the sun at night?
    (*Chorus*) I never did.
Of course, you're right.
How can the sun shine at night
When day begins when it gives light?
    (*Chorus*) Dinga-dinga-doodle,
        dinga-dinga-dite.
It's always day when the sun is bright.

Did you ever see a little boy cry?
    (*Chorus*) Yes, I did.
And so did I.
It seems such a shame for a boy to cry
When he could laugh if he did try.
    (*Chorus*) Dinga-dinga-doodle,
        dinga-dinga-dye,
It's better to laugh than it is to cry.

Did you ever see a rose in the snow?
    (*Chorus*) I never did.
The answer is No.
How can a rose bloom in the snow
When it's too cold for it to grow?
    (*Chorus*) Dinga-dinga-doodle,
        dinga-dow,
A rosebush sleeps when the cold
        winds blow.

(Now sing the following lines:)

I   nev-er saw   a

cow   in the sky.   It   has   no wings with   which to   fly.

I never saw the sun at night;
Day begins when the sun gives light.

I never saw a rose in the snow;
It's too cold for it to grow.

(Go back to the fifth bar for the following chorus:)

Yes, I've seen a little boy cry,
But he could laugh if he did try,

Dinga-dinga-doodle, dinga-dinga-dye,
It's better to laugh than it is to cry.

41

INDEX